# Anthems
# Old &
# New
## for SA Men

**VOLUME ONE**

# Anthems
# Old &
# New
## for SA Men

**100 settings for the
smaller parish choir
selected by Kevin Mayhew**

**VOLUME ONE**

Kevin
Mayhew

We hope you enjoy *Anthems Old & New for SA Men*. Further copies are available from your local music shop or Christian bookshop.

In case of difficulty, please contact the publisher direct by writing to:

The Sales Department
KEVIN MAYHEW LTD
Buxhall
Stowmarket
Suffolk
IP14 3BW

Phone 01449 737978
Fax 01449 737834
E-mail info@kevinmayhewltd.com

Please ask for our complete catalogue of outstanding Church Music.

First published in Great Britain in 1999 by Kevin Mayhew Ltd.

© Copyright 1999 Kevin Mayhew Ltd.

ISBN 1 84003 465 3
ISMN M 57004 616 4
Catalogue No: 1450158

3 4 5 6 7 8 9

Front Cover: A stained glass window, St. Mary's Church, Banbury, Oxfordshire.
Photograph by Derek Forss. Reproduced by kind permission.
Cover design by Jonathan Stroulger.

Music selected by Kevin Mayhew
Music setting by Rob Danter and Donald Thomson
Proof reader: Rachel Judd

# Contents

# Index of Uses

# Anthems

# A CELTIC BENEDICTION

Text: from an old Gaelic prayer
Music: Rodney Bambrick (b.1927)

peace, to the coun-try of the King, to the peace of e-

ter-ni-ty. Ah,

May God shield me, may God fill me,

ah. Praise to the

may God keep me and watch o'er me.

f sostenuto

# AND THE GLORY OF THE LORD

Text: from Scripture
Music: George Frideric Handel (1685-1759) arr. Colin Hand

*Where the text '-ry of' is to be sung to one note, the two syllables should be run together.*

and the glo - ry, the glo - ry of the Lord

glo - ry of the Lord shall be re - vea - led, shall

be re - vea - led, shall be re -

shall be re - veal'd, and the

be re - vea - led, and the

vea - led, and the

Ped.

and all flesh shall see it to-

and all flesh shall see it to-

ge - ther, for the mouth of the Lord hath

Gt.

Ped.

ge - ther, for the mouth of the

- ge - ther, and all flesh shall

spo - ken it, and all flesh shall

spo - ken it, the Lord hath spo - ken it,

mouth of the Lord hath spo - ken it, and all

Lord, and the glo - ry, the glo - ry of the Lord shall be re - vea - led,

Ped. Man.

*ff*

and the glo - ry, the glo - ry, the

flesh, all flesh, shall see it to - ge - ther,

and all flesh shall see it to - ge - ther,

glo - ry of the Lord shall be re - vea - led,

and the glo - ry, the glo - ry of the Lord shall be re -

and the glo - ry, the glo - ry of the Lord shall

Ped.

and all flesh, and all

vea - led, shall be re - vea - led, and all

be re - vea - led, re - vea - led, for the

**Adagio**

the Lord hath spo - ken it.

Lord, the mouth of the Lord hath spo - ken it.

Lord, the mouth of the Lord hath spo - ken it.

*ff*

# AVE MARIA

Text: Luke 1
Music: Jacob Arcadelt (1505-1568) arr. Alan Ridout

be - ne - dic - tus fruc - tus ven - tris tu - i, Je - sus.

tu - i,

San - cta Ma - ri - a, o - ra, o - ra pro no - bis,

san - cta Ma - ri - a, o - ra, o - ra pro no - bis, san -

cta Ma - ri - a, o - ra, o - ra pro no - bis. A - men.

# AVE MARIA

Text: Luke 1
Music: adapted from Johann Sebastian Bach (1685-1750)
by Charles Gounod (1818-1893) arr. Colin Hand

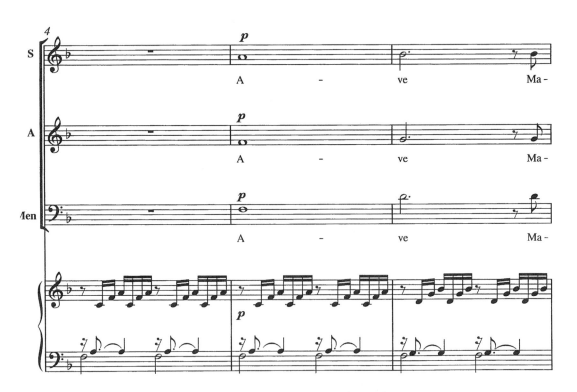

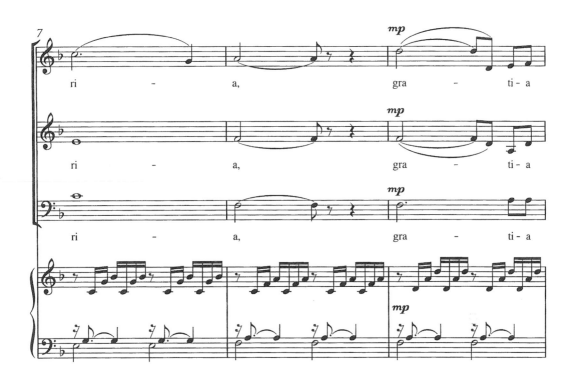

be - ne - dic - ta tu in

be - ne - dic - ta tu in

be - ne - dic - ta tu in

mu - li - e - ri - bus, et be - ne -

mu - li - e - ri - bus, et be - ne -

mu - li - e - ri - bus, et be - ne -

31

*cresc.* *mf* *cresc.*

no - bis pec-ca - to - ri - bus, nunc et in

*cresc.* *mf* *cresc.*

no - bis pec-ca - to - ri-bus, nunc et in

*cresc.* *mf* *cresc.*

no - bis pec-ca - to - ri-bus, nunc et in

*cresc.* *mf* *cresc.*

34

*f* *decresc.*

ho - ra, in ho - ra mor - tis nos - trae.

*f* *decresc.*

ho - ra, in ho - ra mor - tis nos - trae.

*f* *decresc.*

ho - ra, in ho - ra mor - tis nos - trae.

*f* *decresc.*

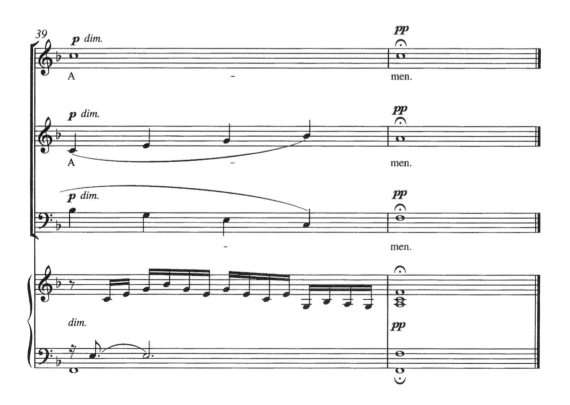

# AVE VERUM CORPUS

Text: 14th century
Music: Wolfgang Amadeus Mozart (1756-1791) arr. Alan Ridout

# Anthems

# BEFORE THE ENDING OF THE DAY

Text: from the Latin, translated by J.M. Neale (1818-1866)
Music: Malcolm Archer (b.1952)

From all ill dreams de-fend our eyes, from night-ly fears and fan-tas-

ies; tread un-der foot our ghost-ly foe, that no pol-lu-tion

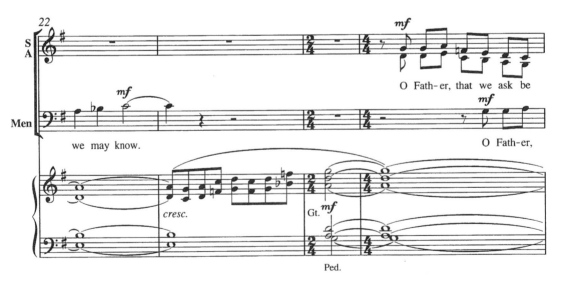

O Fath-er, that we ask be

we may know. O Fath-er,

# BIST DU BEI MIR

Text: Michael Forster (b.1946)
Music: Johann Sebastian Bach (1685-1750) arr. Alan Ridout

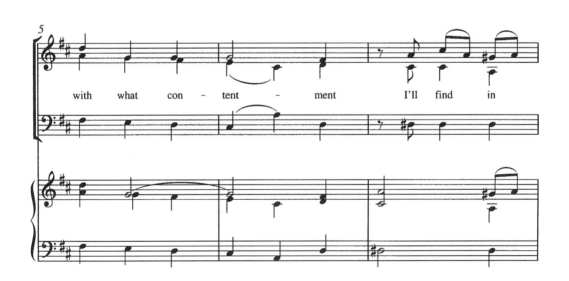

death my life's re - pose. I'll find in death my life's re -

pose. If you are here with what con -

tent - ment I'll find in death my life's re -

pose, I'll     find in death my life's re - pose.

O   sweet  in - deed     would be   my  end - ing

if  you,   in   death my soul be - friend - ing,   with

If you are here with what con-tent - ment I'll find in death my life's re-pose, I'll find in death my life's re-pose.

# Anthems

# BROTHER JAMES' AIR

Text: Psalm 22 (23) from The Scottish Psalter (1650)
Music: James Leith MacBeth Bain (c.1860-1925) arr. Alan Ridout

in the paths of right-eous-ness e'en for his own name's sake, with –
head thou dost with oil a-noint and my cup o - ver flows, my

in the paths of right-eous-ness e'en for his own name's sake.
head thou dost with oil a-noint and my cup o - ver - flows.

Ped.

Sopranos *f*

5. Good –

Altos and Men

Man.

52

ness and mer - cy all my life shall sure - ly fol - low me, and

in God's house for e - ver - more my dwell-ing place shall be, and

in God's house for e - ver - more my dwell-ing place shall be.

# CAN IT BE TRUE?

Text: Nick Fawcett
Music: Morning from 'Peer Gynt' – Edvard Grieg (1843-1907)
arr. Noel Rawsthorne

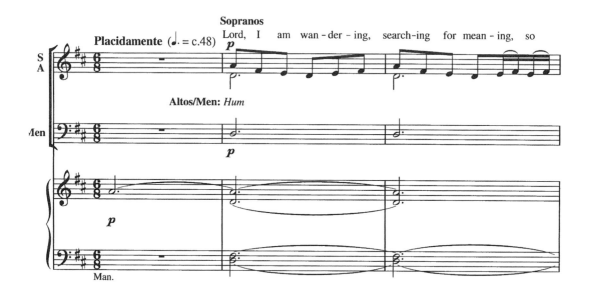

let the truth set you free, find the ful - fil - ment you so long to know.

**Sopranos**

Show me what I must do, let me draw close to you, o - pen my eyes, for too

Man.

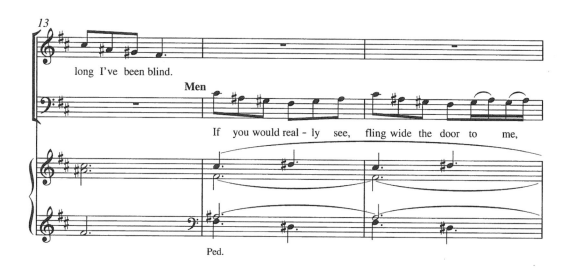

long I've been blind.

**Men**

If you would real - ly see, fling wide the door to me,

Ped.

# CHRIST BE BESIDE ME

Text: James Quinn, SJ (b.1919)
Music: Malcolm Archer (b.1952)

-in me, Christ be be - low me, Christ be a -

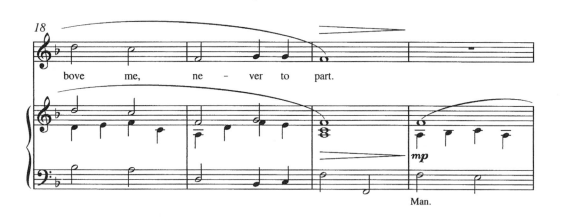

bove me, ne - ver to part.

Man.

Christ on my right hand,

Ped.

Christ on my left hand, Christ all a - round me, shield in the strife. Christ in my sleep - ing, Christ in my sit - ting, Christ in my ris - ing,

# CHRIST BE WITH ME

Text: ascribed to St. Patrick, trans. Cecil Frances Alexander
Music: Canon in D – Johann Pachelbel (1653-1706)
arr. Noel Rawsthorne

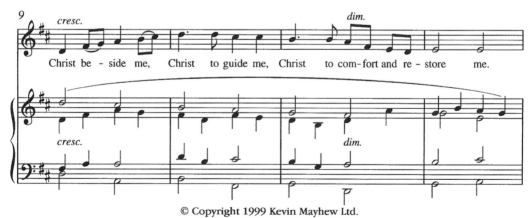

64

Christ in hearts of all that love me, Christ in care of friend and stran - ger.

Christ be - neath me, Christ a - bove me, Christ in qui - et, Christ in dan - ger,

Christ in hearts of all that love me, Christ in care of friend and stran - ger.

*For my friend Billy Adair*

# CHRIST IN CREATION

Text: Joseph M. Plunkett (1887-1916)
Music: Rodney Bambrick (b.1927)

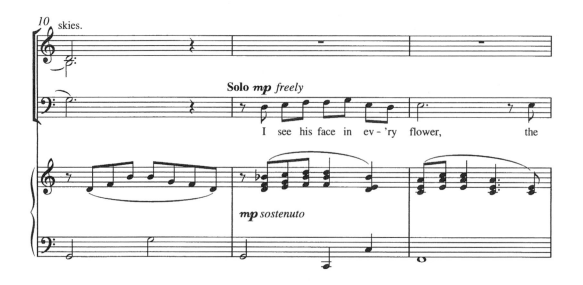

Solo *mp freely*

*mp sostenuto*

I see his face in ev-'ry flower, the

*legato*

thun-der and the sing-ing of the birds are but his voice, and

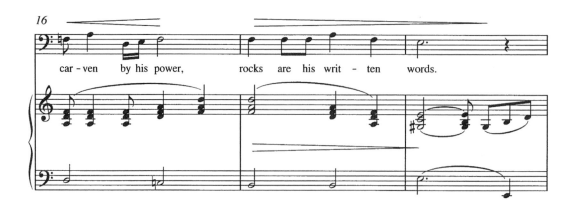

car-ven by his power, rocks are his writ-ten words.

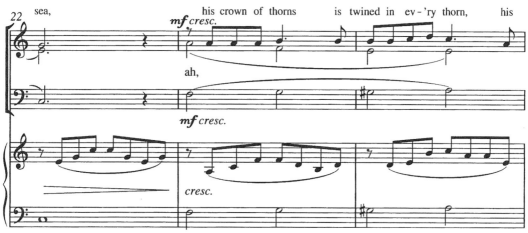

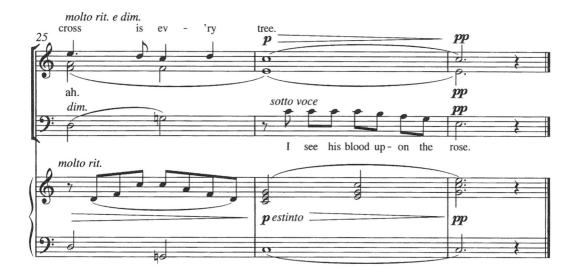

# CHRIST THE WAY OF LIFE

Text: Timothy Dudley-Smith (b.1926)
Music: Norman Warren (b.1934)

1. Christ the way of life poss - ess me, lift my heart to love and praise; guide and keep, sus - tain and bless me, all my days.

2. Well of life, for - e - ver flow - ing, make my bar - ren soul and

bare       like a wa-ter'd gar-den grow — ing

fresh    and    fair.

3. May the tree of life in

splen - dour    from its leaf - y boughs im - part

grace di - vine and heal - ing ten - der, strength of heart.

4. Path of life be - fore me shin - ing, let me come when earth is

4. Path of life be - fore me shin - ing, let me

# COME, HOLY GHOST

Text: John Cosin (1594-1672)
Music: Thomas Attwood (1765-1838) arr. Alan Ridout

life, and fire of love, is com - fort, life, and

fire of love.

Man.

En - a - ble with per - pe - tual light the dull - ness of our

blind - ed sight; a - noint and cheer our soil - ed face

with the a - bun - dance of thy grace. Keep far our foes, give

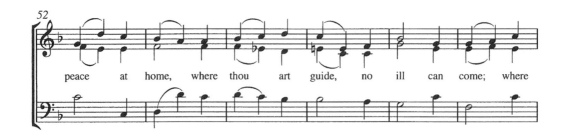

peace at home, where thou art guide, no ill can come; where

thou art guide, no ill can come.

Man.                                    Ped.

*mp*

Teach us to know the Fa - ther, Son, and thee of Both, to

*mp*

be but One; that through the a - ges, all a -

long this may be our end - less song: Praise to

thy e - ter - nal me - rit, Fa - ther, Son, and

Ho - ly Spi - rit, Fa - ther, Son, and Ho - ly Spi - rit.

# COME, LET US ALL THIS DAY

Text: John Troutbeck (1832-1899)
Music: Johann Sebastian Bach (1685-1750) arr. Alan Ridout

God, once more our voi - ces rais - ing. This day the Ho - ly
Ghost he - ro - ic hearts has fired, so let us pray that
ours by him may be in - spired.

praise our God for e - ver true, whose mer - cies are this

day, and ev - 'ry morn - ing new.

# Anthems

# COME, MY WAY, MY TRUTH, MY LIFE

Text: George Herbert (1593-1632)
Music: Malcolm Archer (b.1952)

ends all strife: such a Life as kill-

such a Life as kill-

-eth death.

-eth death.

**Sopranos and Altos**

*mp*

Come, my Light, my Feast, my Strength; such a

Add

Man. 1

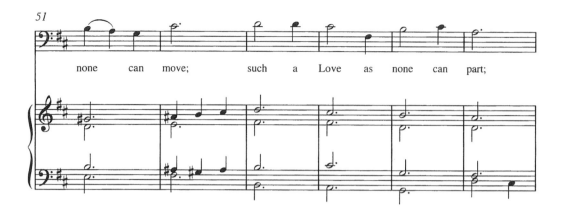

none can move; such a Love as none can part;

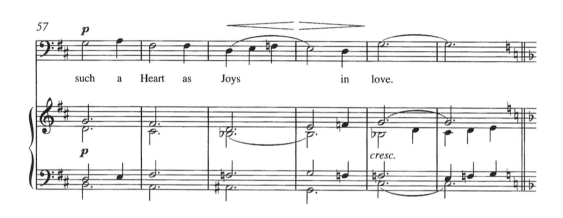

such a Heart as Joys in love.

Come, my Way, my Truth, my Life:

Come, my Way, my Truth, my Life: such a

such a Way as gives us breath; such a
Way as gives us breath; such a Truth as
Truth as ends all strife; such a Life as kill -
ends all strife; such a Life as kill -
- eth death. A - men.

# COMFORT, COMFORT

Text: Nick Fawcett, based on Isaiah 40:1-2
Music: Adagio from Violin Concerto in G minor – Max Bruch (1838-1920)
arr. Noel Rawsthorne

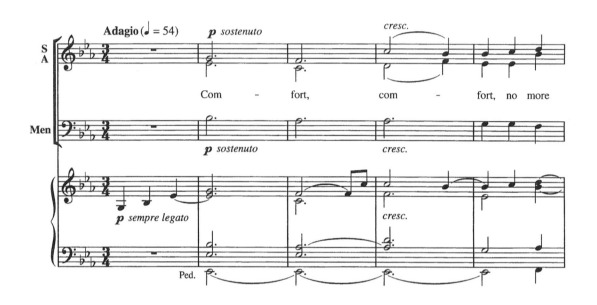

love now will lift you up; the fut-ure calls, let's start a-

gain.

Put the past be-hind, let go of all your

hid-den doubts and fears.

**Sopranos** *mp*

Come to me and find new mean-ing shin-ing

through the pain and tears.

Come then,

come then, no more sor - row, you'll find joy to - mor -

row, for I shall res - tore you and lift you up; the fut - ure calls, let's start a - gain.

# Anthems

*For the Durham Diocesan Choirs*

# CRY OUT WITH JOY TO THE LORD

Text: Psalm 100
Music: Richard Lloyd (b.1933)

Cry out with joy to the Lord, all the earth; serve the Lord with glad - ness; come be - fore him, come be - fore him,

sing - ing, sing - ing, sing - ing for joy.

sing - - - ing for joy.

* Voices may divide with Sopranos and Tenors singing the top notes and Altos and Basses singing the lower notes.

* Divisions for Sopranos and Altos.
  Alternatively, Sopranos may sing the notes with downward stems.

serve the Lord with glad - ness; come be-fore him,

come be-fore him, sing - ing, sing - ing, sing - ing,

sing - ing for joy, sing - ing,

sing - ing for joy.

Man.

Ped.

# EXPECTANS EXPECTAVI

Text: Charles Hamilton Sorley
Music: Charles Wood (1866-1926) arr. Alan Ridout

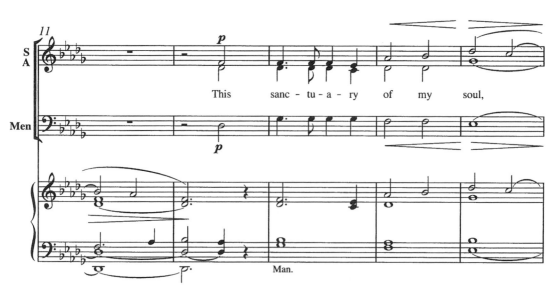

un - wit - ting I keep pure and whole, un - latched and lit, if lit, if thou thou should'st care to en - ter or to tar -

vice de – di – cate.

My

soul, keep pure and whole.

# Anthems

# FATHER, WE HAVE BROKEN THE BREAD

Text: Scottish Liturgy (1982)
Music: Christopher Tambling (b.1964)

# FATHER, YOUR STEADFAST PURPOSE

Text: from the Scottish Liturgy
Music: Christopher Tambling (b.1964)

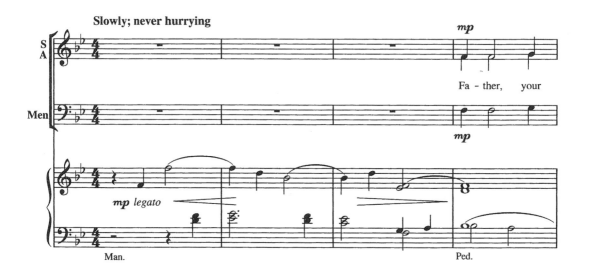

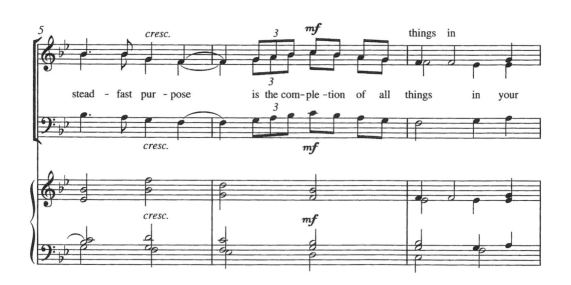

son. May we who have re - ceived the pled-ges of the king - dom, live by

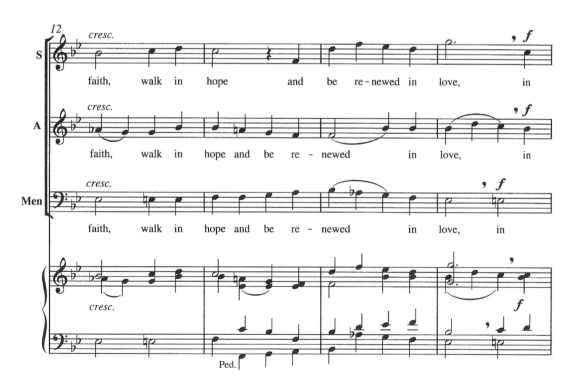

S faith, walk in hope and be re-newed in love, in

A faith, walk in hope and be re - newed in love, in

Men faith, walk in hope and be re - newed in love, in

116

all in all; through Je - sus

all in all; through Je - sus Christ our

all in all; through Je - sus Christ our Lord. A -

Christ, through Je - sus Christ our Lord. A - men.

Lord, through Je - sus Christ our Lord. A - men.

men, through Je - sus Christ our Lord. A - men.

*For John R. Turner and the choir of Glasgow Cathedral*

# FILL THOU MY LIFE

Text: Horatius Bonar (1808-1889)
Music: Richard Lloyd (b.1933)

ways.

Not for the lip of praise a-lone, nor ev'n the prais-ing heart I ask, but for a life made up of praise in ev-'ry part.

Man.

Ped.

Praise in the com-mon things of life, its go — ings out and in;

praise in each du - ty and each deed, how - e - ver small and mean.

Man.

dim.

Ped.

So shalt thou, gra - cious Lord, from me re - ceive the glo - ry

Man.

So shall no part of day or night from sa - cred-ness be free; but all my life, in ev - 'ry

# FROM GLORY TO GLORY

Text: Liturgy of St James trans. Charles Humphreys (1840-1921)
Music: Richard Shephard (b.1949)

Thanks - giv - ing and glo - ry and

**Sopranos**
*mf*

wor - ship and bles - sing and love, one heart and one

song have the saints up - on earth and a - bove.

# GLADNESS, SADNESS, JOY AND SORROW

*Introit*
Text: Nick Fawcett
Music: To a Wild Rose – Edward MacDowell (1861-1908)
arr. Noel Rawsthorne

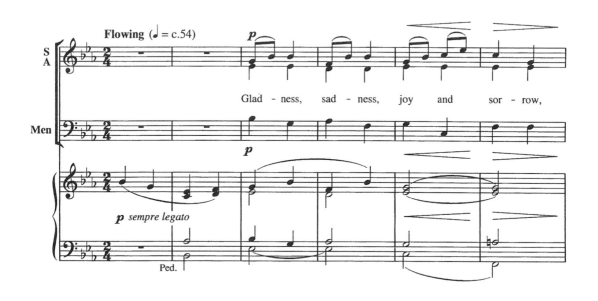

# GOD IS A SPIRIT

Text: John 4:24
Music: William Sterndale Bennett (1816-1875) arr. Alan Ridout

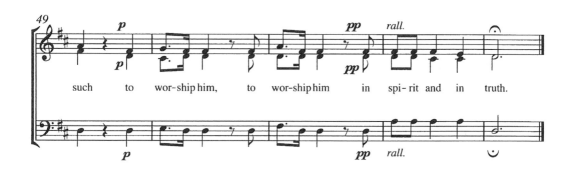

# GOD IS WHY I AM

Text: Brian Foley (b.1919)
Music: Alan Viner (b.1951)

*Optional organ accompaniment*

# GOD SO LOVED THE WORLD

Text: John 3:16
Music: John Stainer (1840-1901) arr. Alan Ridout

life, e - ver - las - ting, e - ver - las - ting

life. God so loved the world, God

so loved the world, God so loved the world.

# Anthems

# GOD THAT MADEST EARTH AND HEAVEN

Text: Reginald Heber (1783-1826) and Richard Whatley (1787-1863)
Music: Horatio William Parker (1863-1919) arr. Alan Ridout

# GO IN PEACE

Text: Nick Fawcett
Music: Largo from 'New World' Symphony – Antonín Dvořák (1841-1904)
arr. Noel Rawsthorne

hard to bear; he'll be with you, see you through, let peace fill you,

soft as dew, soft as dew, soft as dew.

# GREAT AND MARVELLOUS

Text: Revelation 15:3-4
Music: Henry Smart (1813-1879) arr. Alan Ridout

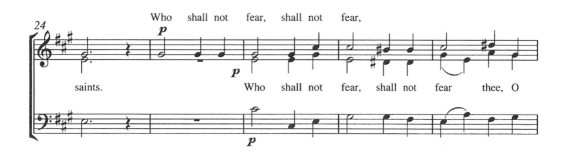

# HALLELUJAH CHORUS

Text: from Scripture
Music: George Frideric Handel (1685-1759) arr. Colin Hand

God om-ni-po-tent reign-eth, hal-le-lu-jah, hal-le-lu-jah, hal-le-

God om-ni-po-tent reign-eth, hal-le-lu-jah, hal-le-lu-jah, hal-le-

God om-ni-po-tent reign-eth, hal-le-lu-jah, hal-le-lu-jah, hal-le-

*non legato*

Reeds

Man.

lu-jah, hal-le-lu-jah, for the Lord God om-ni-po-tent

lu-jah, hal-le-lu-jah, for the Lord God om-ni-po-tent

lu-jah, hal-le-lu-jah, for the Lord God om-ni-po-tent

Reeds off

Ped.

reign - eth, hal-le - lu-jah, hal-le - lu -jah, hal-le - lu -jah, hal-le - lu-jah,

reign - eth, hal-le - lu-jah, hal-le - lu -jah, hal-le - lu -jah, hal-le - lu-jah,

reign - eth, hal-le - lu-jah, hal-le - lu -jah, hal-le - lu -jah, hal-le - lu-jah,

Reeds

Reeds off

Man.

for the Lord God om-ni - po-tent reign - eth, hal-le-

hal-le-lu-jah, hal-le - lu - jah, hal-le-lu-jah,

hal-le-lu-jah, hal-le - lu-jah, hal - le - lu - jah,

hal - le - lu - jah, hal - le - lu - jah, hal - le - lu - jah, hal -

God om - ni - po - tent reign - eth, hal - le - lu - jah, hal -

lu - jah, hal - le - lu - jah, hal - le - lu - jah, hal - le -

le - lu - jah! The king - dom of this

le - lu - jah! The king - dom of this

lu - jah! The king - dom of this

world    is be - come the king-dom of our Lord and of his

world    is be - come the king-dom of our Lord and of his

world    is be - come the king-dom of our Lord and of his

Gt. *f*

Christ, and of his Christ;

Christ, and of his Christ;      and

Christ, and of his Christ; and he shall reign for e - ver and e - ver,

(+ Man. ad lib.)

160

e-ver,      hal-le-lu-jah, hal-le - lu-jah, and he    shall

e-ver,    and Lord of   lords,    hal-le-lu-jah,    hal-le - lu-jah,     and

e-ver,    and Lord of   lords,    hal-le-lu-jah,    hal-le - lu-jah, and he    shall

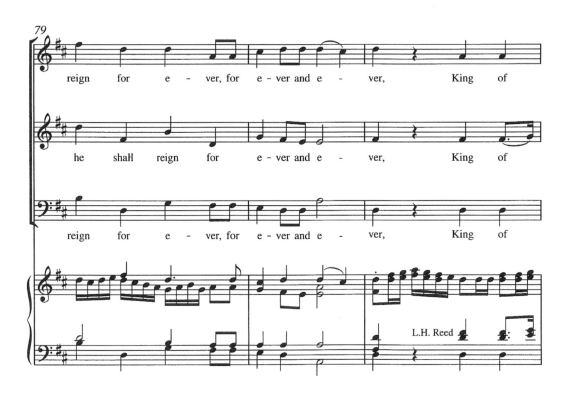

reign    for     e -    ver, for   e - ver and e    -    ver,      King     of

he   shall   reign     for     e - ver and e    -    ver,      King     of

reign    for     e -    ver, for   e - ver and e    -    ver,      King     of

L.H. Reed

ver,      King   of   kings,    and Lord   of   lords,     hal-le-lu-jah,    hal-le-

ver,      for e-ver   and   e-ver,    for e-ver   and   e-ver,    hal-le-lu-jah,    hal-le-

ver,      for e-ver   and   e-ver,    for e-ver   and   e-ver,    hal-le-lu-jah,    hal-le-

lu-jah,    hal-le-lu-jah,    hal-le-lu-jah,     hal - le - lu - jah!

lu-jah,    hal-le-lu-jah,    hal-le-lu-jah,     hal - le - lu - jah!

lu-jah,    hal-le-lu-jah,    hal-le-lu-jah,     hal - le - lu - jah!

# HE SHALL FEED HIS FLOCK

Text: from Scripture
Music: George Frideric Handel (1685-1759) arr. Colin Hand

shep - herd, and he shall ga - ther the lambs with his arm,

shep - herd, and he shall ga - ther the lambs with his arm,

shep - herd, and he shall ga - ther the lambs with his arm,

with his arm. He shall feed his flock like a

with his arm. He shall feed his flock like a

with his arm. He shall feed his flock like a

shep - herd, and he shall ga - ther the lambs with his arm,

shep - herd, and he shall ga - ther the lambs with his arm,

shep - herd, and he shall ga - ther the lambs with his arm,

with his arm, and car - ry them

with his arm. and car - ry them

with his arm. and car - ry them

in his bo - som,     and gen - tly lead     those     that are     with young,     and

in his bo - som,     and gen - tly lead     those     that are     with young,     and

in his bo - som,     and gen - tly lead     those     that are     with young,     and

gen - tly lead     those,     and gen - tly lead     those that are     with young.

gen - tly lead     those, and     gen - tly     lead     those that are     with young.

lead     those,     and gen - tly     lead     those that are     with young.

he will give you rest.  Come un - to him, all

he will give you rest.  Come un - to him, all

he will give you rest.  Come un - to him, all

ye that la - bour, come un - to him, ye that are hea - vy la - den, and

ye that la - bour, come un - to him, ye that are hea - vy la - den, and

ye that la - bour, come un - to him, ye that are hea - vy la - den, and

he will give you rest. Take his yoke u-pon you,

he will give you rest. Take his yoke u-pon you, and

he will give you rest. and

learn of him, and low - ly of heart, and

learn of him, for he is meek and low - ly of heart, and

learn of him, for he is meek and low - ly of heart,

and low - ly of heart, and ye shall find rest, and

he is meek and low - ly of heart, and ye shall find rest, and

he is meek and low - ly of heart, and

ye shall find rest un - to your souls.

ye shall find rest un - to your souls.

ye shall find rest un - to your souls.

# HOLY SPIRIT, GIFT DIVINE

*Pentecost Anthem*
Text: Nick Fawcett
Music: Chanson Triste – Peter Ilyich Tchaikovsky (1840-1893)
arr. Noel Rawsthorne

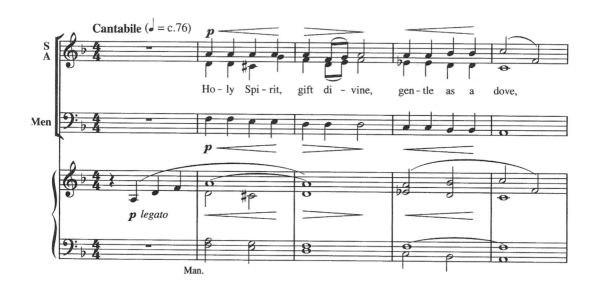

May we hear your still, small voice speak-ing of your pur - pose.

Weak or migh - ty, slave or free, give us eyes that we may see

all you want our lives to be; res - pond now to our plea.

fill us to your glo - ry. Guid - ing, a - bid - ing, come,

make us new, that all we do may hon - our you.

Ho - ly Spi - rit, fall a - fresh, come as tongues of fire,

grant re - new - al  to  all  flesh,  come  in - spire.

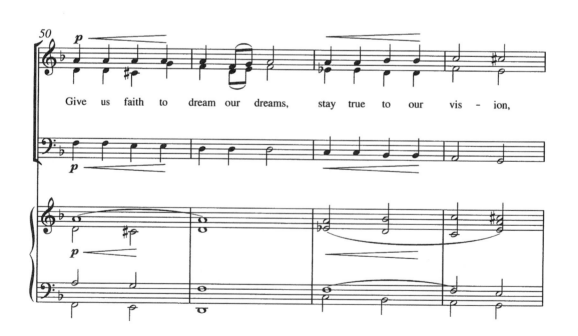

Give  us  faith  to  dream  our  dreams,  stay  true  to  our  vis - ion,

male or fe - male, young or old, keep our hearts from grow - ing cold,

in Christ's ser - vice make us bold, his king - dom to un - fold.

# HONOUR AND MAJESTY

Text: Psalm 96:6
Music: Maurice Green (1695-1755) arr. Alan Ridout

# Anthems

# HOW BEAUTEOUS ARE THEIR FEET

Text: Isaac Watts (1674-1748)
Music: Charles Villiers Stanford (1852-1924) arr. Alan Ridout

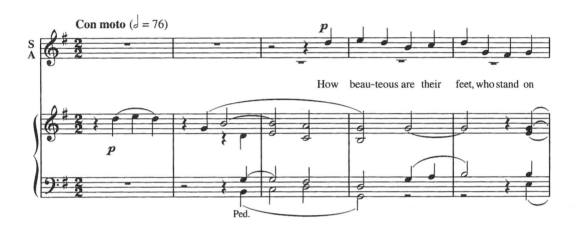

died with - out the sight.

The Lord makes

bare his arm through all the earth a - broad; the

The Lord makes bare his arm through all the

Lord makes bare his arm through all the earth a -

191

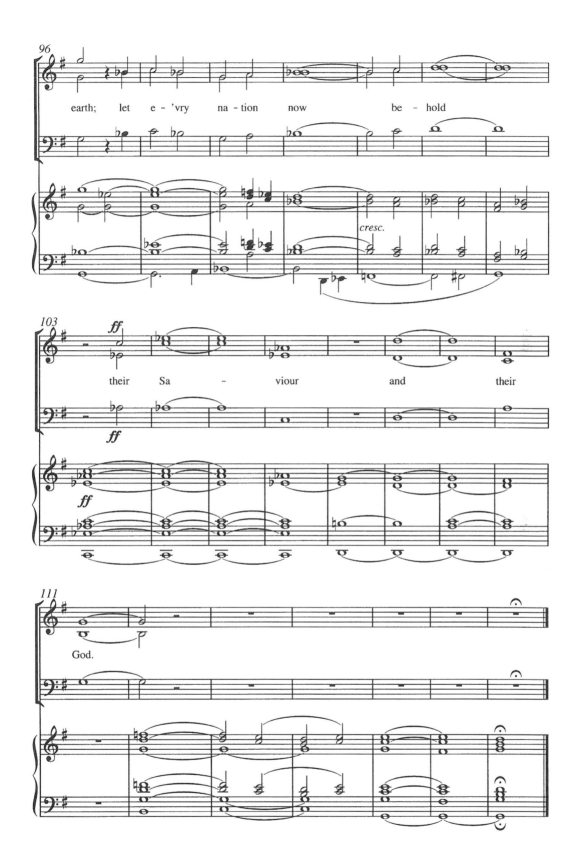

earth; let e - 'vry na - tion now be - hold

their Sa - viour and their

God.

# HOW BEAUTIFUL UPON THE MOUNTAINS

Text: Isaiah 52:7
Music: John Stainer (1840-1901) arr. Alan Ridout

# I AM THE BREAD OF LIFE

Text: John 6:35
Music: Noel Rawsthorne (b.1929)

*In memory of Great Aunt Winifred*

# I GIVE YOU MY HANDS, LORD

Text: adapted from Grail
Music: Christopher Tambling (b.1964)

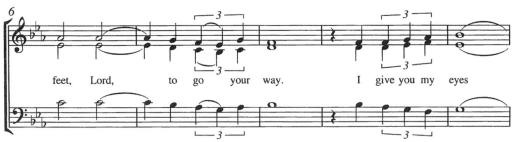

# IN AN UPPER ROOM

*Eucharistic Hymn*
Text: Nick Fawcett
Music: Prelude in C minor – Frédéric Chopin (1810-1849)
arr. Noel Rawsthorne

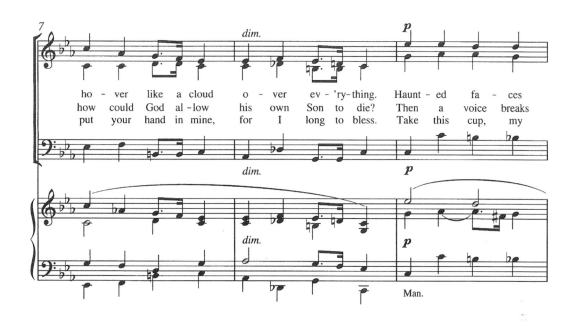

ho - ver like a cloud o - ver ev - 'ry-thing. Haunt - ed fa - ces
how could God al - low his own Son to die? Then a voice breaks
put your hand in mine, for I long to bless. Take this cup, my

Man.

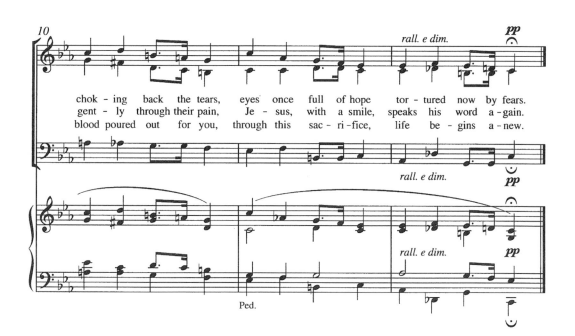

chok - ing back the tears, eyes once full of hope tor - tured now by fears.
gent - ly through their pain, Je - sus, with a smile, speaks his word a - gain.
blood poured out for you, through this sac - ri - fice, life be - gins a - new.

Ped.

# Anthems

# INCLINE THINE EAR

Text: Psalm 31:2
Music: Friedrich Heinrich Himmel (1765-1814) arr. Alan Ridout

# JESU, JOY OF OUR DESIRING

Text: Robert Bridges (1844-1930)
Music: Johann Sebastian Bach (1685-1750) arr: Alan Ridout

1. Je - su, joy of our de -
2. Through the way where hope is

life im - pas - sioned
ho - liest trea - sure:

stri - ving still to truth un - known,
thou dost e - ver lead thine own

soar - ing, dy - ing round thy
in the love of joys un -

210

throne.
known.

*Last time*

211

# JESU, THE VERY THOUGHT OF THEE

Text: 12th century, trans. Edward Caswall (1814-1878)
Music: Richard Lloyd (b.1933)

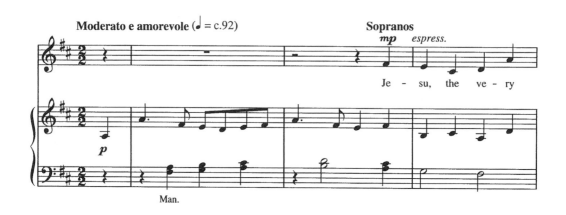

rest, and in thy pre - sence rest.

**Men**
*mp espress.*

O hope of ev - 'ry con - trite heart. O joy of all the
Man. Ped.

meek, to those who ask how kind thou art, how

good to those who seek, how good to those who seek!

through e - ter - ni - ty, e - ter - ni - ty, and

through e - ter - ni - ty, and through e - ter - ni - ty, and

through e - ter - ni - ty.

Thee, Je - su, may our voi - ces bless, thee

# KING OF GLORY, KING OF PEACE

Text: George Herbert (1593-1632)
Music: John Marsh (b.1939)

grant - ed my re - quest, thou hast heard me; thou didst

note my work-ing breast, thou hast spared me.

Where - fore with my ut - most

mf

Gt. Fl.

mf
Sw.

plied, thou didst hear me.

Sev'n whole days, not one in sev'n, I will praise thee; in my heart tho' not in heav'n, I can

raise thee. Small it is, in this poor sort to en-

rol thee: e'en e - ter - ni-ty's too short to ex-

tol thee, to ex - tol thee.

*molto rall.*

*ff*

# LAUDATE DOMINUM

Text: Psalm 117
Music: Wolfgang Amadeus Mozart (1756-1791) arr. Colin Hand

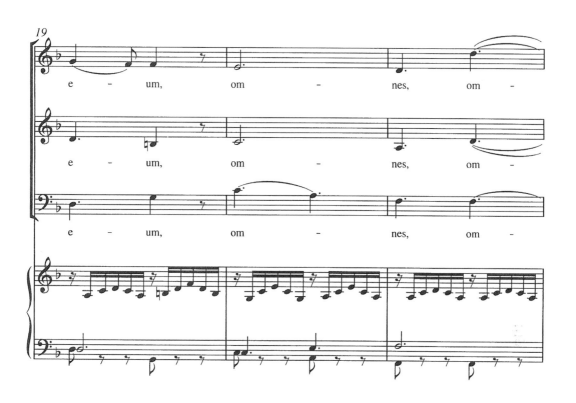

e - um, om - nes, om -

e - um, om - nes, om -

e - um, om - nes, om -

- nes po - pu - li.

- nes po - pu - li.

- nes po - pu - li.

Solo

mp

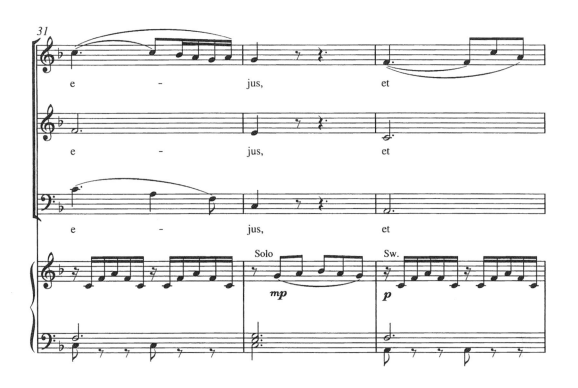

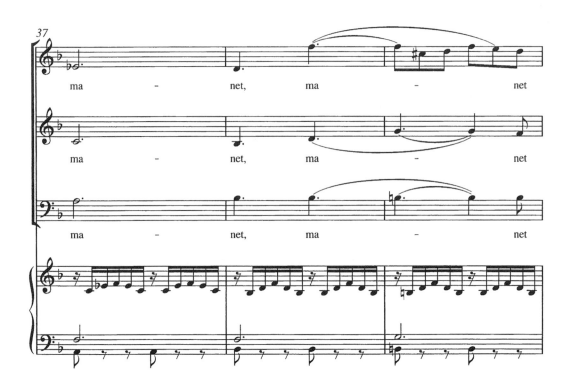

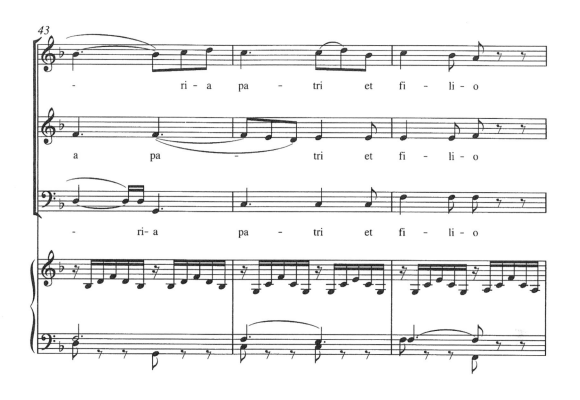

# LAUDATE DOMINUM

Text: Psalm 150
Music: Giuseppe Ottavio Pitoni (1657-1743) arr. Alan Ridout

Lau - da - te e - um
ci - tha - ra. Lau - da - te e - um in cym - ba - lis be - ne - so -

lau - det Do -
nan - ti - bus: om - nis spi - ri - tus lau - det

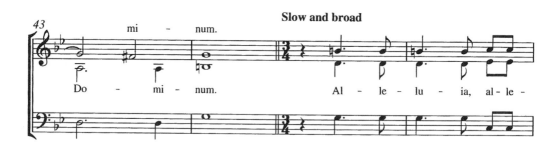

**Slow and broad**

mi - num.
Do - mi - num. Al - le - lu - ia, al - le -

lu - ia, al - le - lu - ia, al - le - lu - ia,

al - le - lu - ia, al - le - lu - ia.

# LAY NOT UP FOR YOURSELVES

Text: Matthew 6:19-20
Music: John Bacchus Dykes (1823-1876) arr. Alan Ridout

# LEAD ME, LORD

Text: Psalm 5:8; 4:9
Music: Samuel Sebastian Wesley (1810-1876) arr. Alan Ridout

# LEAD ME, O LORD

Text and Music: Andrew Gant (b.1963)

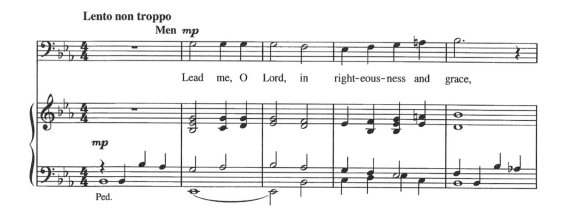

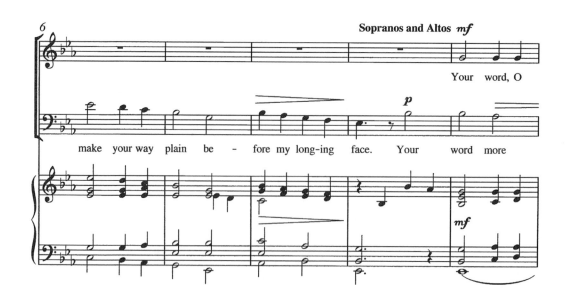

# LET ALL NATIONS CLAP THEIR HANDS

Text: Psalm 47
Music: Christopher Tambling (b.1964)

Lord is high and to be a-dored, the great King o-ver all the earth. He is gone up with shouts of joy. the trum-pet sounds as the Lord as-cends:

O sing prai-ses to our God, sing prai-ses to our King. For God is King of all the earth, his migh-ty acts shall be pro - claimed: the

# LIFT UP YOUR HEADS, O YE GATES

Text: from Scripture
Music: George Frideric Handel (1685-1759) arr. Colin Hand

257

is the King of Glo-ry, he is the King of Glo-ry,

is the King of Glo-ry, he is the King of Glo-ry,

is the King of Glo-ry, he is the King of Glo-ry,

of Glo - ry.

of Glo - ry.

of Glo - ry.

Ped.

258

# LIFT UP YOUR HEADS

Text: George Weissel (1590-1635)
translated by Catherine Winkworth (1827-1878)
Music: John Marsh (b.1939)

**With breadth and movement**

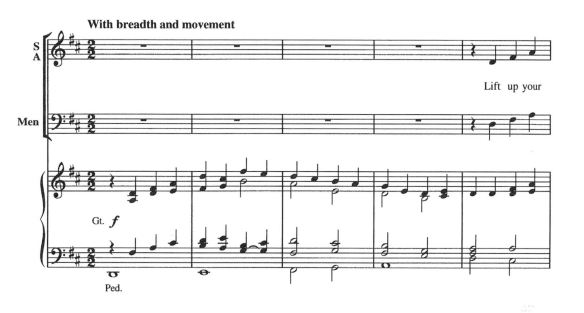

King of kings is draw-ing near, the Sa-viour of the world is here.

**Sopranos**
*p legato*

O blest the land, the ci - ty blest

Sw. *p*

Man.

*cresc.*

where Christ the ru - ler is con - fessed. O hap-py hearts and hap-py

*cresc.*

homes to whom this king in tri-umph comes.

Fling wide the

heart, make

por - tals of your heart, make it a tem - ple set a -

part   from   earth-ly   use        for heav'ns em - ploy,        a -

dorned with prayer and    love   and   joy.

poco allarg.   **Maestoso**   Come,

Come, Sa-viour,

# LIVING GOD, I CRY TO YOU

Text: Nick Fawcett, based on Psalm 77
Music: Air from Suite No. 3 in D – Johann Sebastian Bach (1685-1750)
arr. Noel Rawsthorne

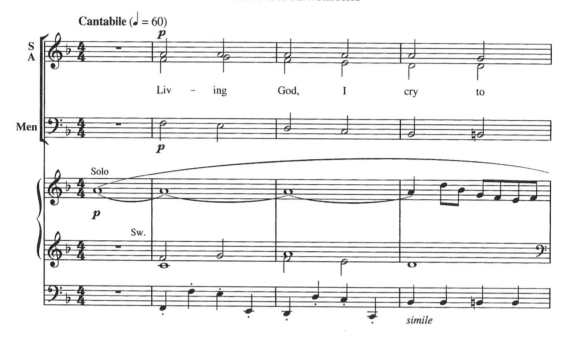

prayer,      weak  and  wea –  ry,    show  me  that  you

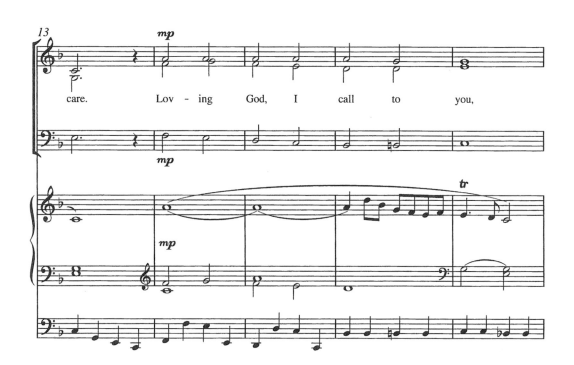

care.     Lov – ing  God,  I    call   to     you,

in  your  good - ness,  hear  my  cry,

bruised  and  bro - ken,  lift  my  spi - rit  high.

Though I seek and do not seem to find,

still your wond — rous deeds I call to mind,

e – ver gra – cious, e – ver kind.

Heav'n and earth, your name con – fess,

sov - 'reign in your ho - li - ness,

swift to save and sure to bless.

In my dark - ness, you will be my light,

dawn will come and put an end to night,

tears     and     fears,     at     last     put     to     flight.

Liv - ing     God,     I     cry     to     you,

of – fer you my faith made new,

take my hand and lead me through.

*Commissioned by Mrs. Janet Townend, for the choir and organists of St.Andrew's Church, Bostal Heath, Abbey Wood*

# LO! GOD IS HERE

Text: G. Tersteegen (1697-1769), translated by John Wesley (1703-1791)
Music: Philip Moore (b.1943)

# Anthems

# LORD, I LIFT MY HANDS TO YOU

Text: Nick Fawcett
Music: Adagio from Pathétique Sonata – Ludwig van Beethoven (1770-1827)
arr. Noel Rawsthorne

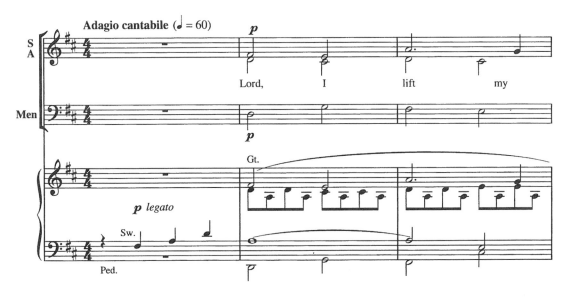

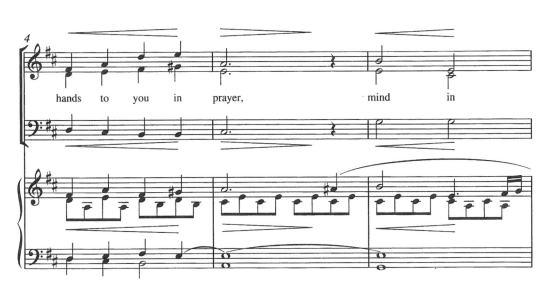

tur - moil, heart crushed by care.

Men
Come to me and find rest for your soul. Don't

wor - ry, simp-ly trust me, my love can make you

# LORD, I WOULD SERVE YOU

*Penitential Hymn*
Text: Nick Fawcett
Music: Adagietto from Symphony No. 5 – Gustav Mahler (1860-1911)
arr. Noel Rawsthorne

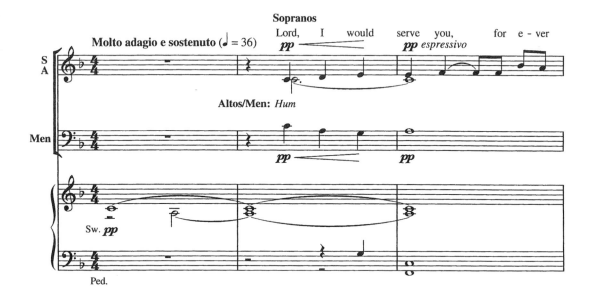

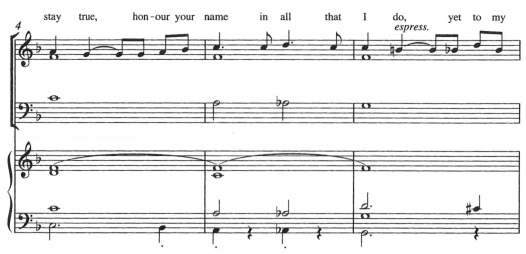

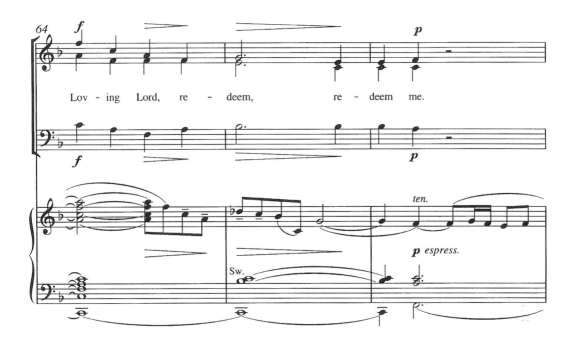

Lov - ing Lord, re - deem, re - deem me.

# LORD OF ALL

Text: Cyril Alington (1872-1955)
Music: Malcolm Archer (b.1952)

Lord, the way to sin - ners shown, Lord, the truth by

on the throne. Je - su,

sin - ners known, love in - car - nate on the throne, Je -

Je - su,

hear and save.

su, hear and save.

hear and save.

293

# Anthems

# LORD OF ALL HOPEFULNESS

Text: Jan Struther (1901-1953)
Music: Malcolm Archer (b.1952)

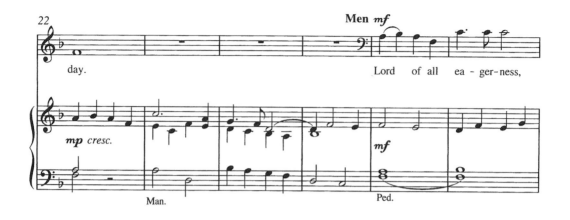

day.

Men *mf*

Lord of all ea - ger-ness,

*mp cresc.*

Man.

*mf*

Ped.

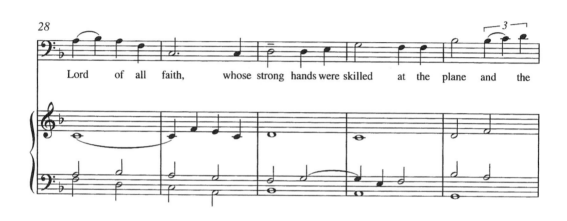

Lord of all faith, whose strong hands were skilled at the plane and the

S
A

be there at our la - bours and give us, we pray your strength in our

Men

lathe, *mf*

hearts, Lord, at the noon of the day.

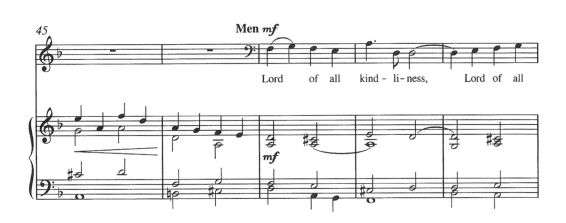

**Men** *mf*

Lord of all kind - li - ness, Lord of all

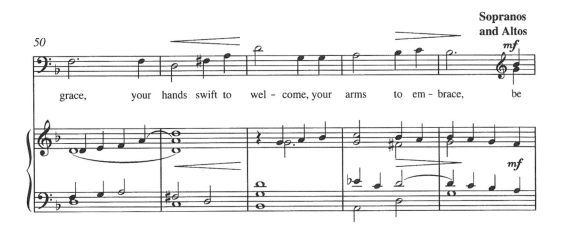

**Sopranos and Altos** *mf*

grace, your hands swift to wel - come, your arms to em - brace, be

there at our ho - ming, and give us, we pray, your love in our

hearts, Lord, at the eve of the day. Lord of all gen - tle - ness,

Lord of all calm, whose voice is con - tent - ment, whose pre - sence is

# LORD OF OUR FATHERS

Text: Michael Forster (b.1946)
Music: Colin Mawby (b.1936)

al - le - lu - ia, al - le - lu - ia!

Hea-ven it-self, with pro-mised grace, makes with the earth a meet-ing place;

Man.

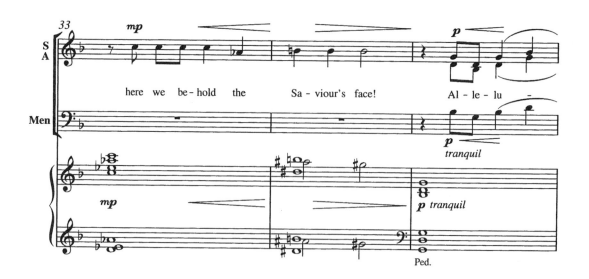

here we be-hold the Sa - viour's face! Al - le - lu -

Men

tranquil

tranquil

Ped.

jus - tice heard, mak - ing the voice of jus - tice heard!

Al - le - lu - ia, al - le - lu - ia,

al - le - lu - ia, al - le - lu - ia, al - le - lu - ia,

Man.

# LORD, WE ADORE YOU

Text: Michael Forster (b.1946)
Music: Colin Mawby (b.1936)

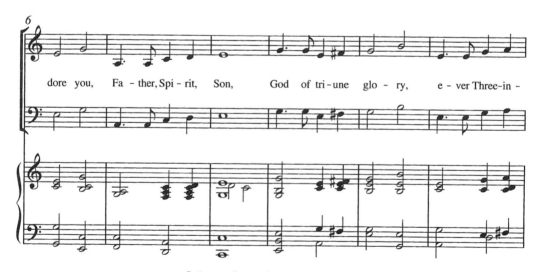

God of tri - une glo - ry, e - ver Three-in - One! 'Ho - ly, ho - ly,

ho - ly!' hear the se - raphs cry; 'Ho - ly, ho - ly, ho - ly!'

let the earth re - ply! True Son and Fa - ther now we re - cog-nise,

fied in di-verse cre - a - tion, ful - ly u - ni - fied.

In the Ho - ly Spi - rit is the pro-mise sealed; now in tri -une

glo - ry be all truth re - vealed! Lord, we a - dore you, Fa - ther, Spi - rit,

Son, God of tri-une glo-ry, e-ver Three-in-One!

'Ho-ly, ho-ly, ho-ly!' hear the se-raphs cry; 'Ho-ly, ho-ly,

ho-ly!' let the earth re-ply!

Tuba

*For the Durham Methodists*

# LOVE DIVINE!

Text: Charles Wesley (1707-1788)
Music: Richard Lloyd (b. 1933)

tem - ples leave.

Thee we would be al - ways bles - sing, serve thee as thy hosts a - bove; pray, and praise thee,

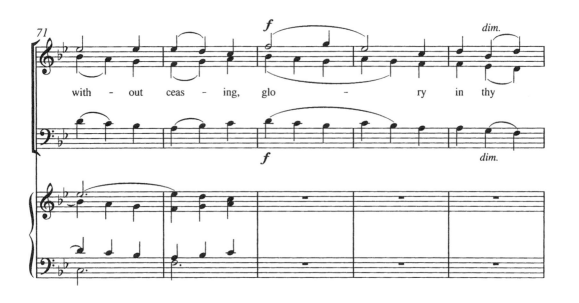

with - out ceas - ing, glo - ry in thy

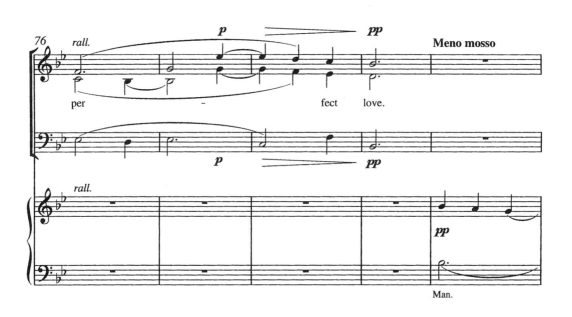

per - fect love.

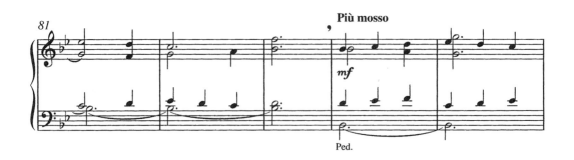

perfectly restored in thee.

Changed from glory into glory,

till in heav'n we take our place; till we

cast our crowns be - fore thee, lost in

won - der, love, and praise!

Lost in won - der, love, and praise!

321

*For Michael Forster and the Chapel Choir of Wellington School*

# LOVE OF THE FATHER

Text: Robert Seymour Bridges (1844-1930)
Music: Richard Lloyd (b.1933)

strife, cre - a - tion's whole de - sire and breath of life.

Thou the all ho - ly, thou su -

Man.

preme in might, thou dost give peace,

Ped.

thy pre - sence ma - keth right;

thou with thy fa - vour all things dost en - fold,

*mp* thou with thy fa - vour all things dost en - fold, with

Man.

thine all - kind - ness free from harm wilt hold.

Ped.

Hope of all com-fort, splen-dour of all aid, that dost not fail nor leave the heart a-fraid; to all that cry thou dost all help ac-cord, the an-gels' ar-mour, and the saints' re-ward.

* optional accompaniment

wor-shipped e - ver - more, e - ver -more: us whom thou mad-est, com - fort

wor-shipped e - ver - more: us whom thou mad - est, com - fort with thy

wor-shipped e - ver - more: us whom thou mad - est, com - fort with thy

with thy might, and lead us to en - joy thy heav'n - ly light,

might, and lead us to en - joy thy heav'n - ly light,

might, and lead us to en - joy thy heav'n - ly light,

and lead us to en-

joy thy heav'n - ly light.

# MY JESUS, O WHAT WEIGHT OF WOE

Text: Unknown
Music: Johann Sebastian Bach (1685-1750) arr. Alan Ridout

wretch – ed – ness of mor – tal man, thou
pier – ced hands, thy shame – ful death, for

hast for us en – dur – ed. In
me have brought sal – va – tion. The

pain, in grief, trem – blest thou be – neath thy
cross, the grave, thou from hea – ven came to

bur – den and to hea – ven
suf – fer, gra – cious Sa – viour,

lift – est hands in sup – pli – ca – tion.
how can man for – get thy pas – sion.

# NON NOBIS

Text and Music: Andrew Gant (b.1963)

1. Je – sus sat at Ma - ry's side at close of eve – ning, the dis -
2. Si – mon Pe – ter dragged his nets from out the wa – ter, Je - sus

ci - ples stood a - ston - ished as the wa - ter turned to wine.
told him, 'Cast a - gain, friend,' so they sailed a mile from land.

'Ma - ry, Ma - ry, what is this thing that we are see - ing?' Ma - ry
'Pe - ter, Pe - ter, this catch is great, our nets are break - ing!' Pe - ter

smiled then, say - ing quiet - ly, 'Friends, the praise should not be
an - swered, 'Just be - lieve, friends, we are in God's migh - ty

*Refrain*
**Full choir** *mf*

mine.'
hand.'

Non no - bis, non no - bis, give the glo - ry to the

*mf*

**Men** *mf*

3. Thou - sands  ga - thered to  hear the bles - sed voice of  Je - sus, then a

child  came with an  off - 'ring, two small fish  and  loaves of  bread.

**Sopranos and Altos** *mf*

'Mas - ter,  Mas - ter; these  things  are thine if they will  feed  us,' the dis -

ci - ples  took and broke  them, and the  mul - ti - tude was  fed.

Refrain

Non no-bis, non no-bis, give the glo-ry to our Lord and King,

non no-bis, non no-bis, still his prai - ses sing.

Do what-so - e - ver he bids you,

Non no-bis, non no-bis, give the glo-ry to the Son of Man,

Non no-bis, non no-bis, give the glo-ry to the Son of Man,

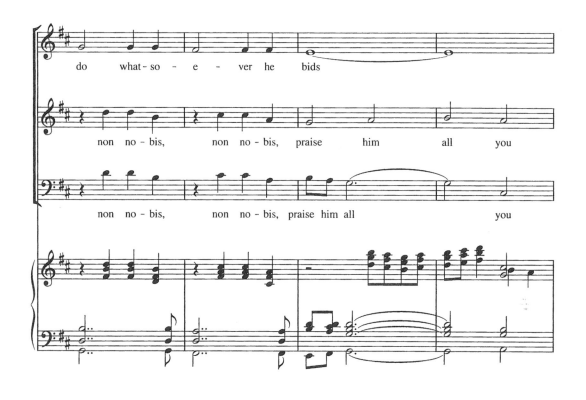

# Anthems

# NOW IS ETERNAL LIFE

Text: George Wallace Briggs (1875-1959)
Music: Richard Lloyd (b.1933)

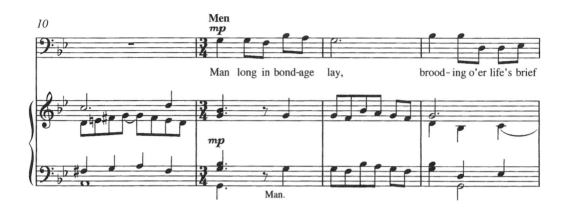

Man long in bond-age lay, brood-ing o'er life's brief

Man.

was it, O God, for naught, for naught thou ma-dest

span;

man? Thou art our hope, our vi-tal breath; shall hope un-dy - ing

Ped.

high; who lives in him shall ne - ver die.

**Poco meno mosso**
**All voices in unison**

Un - fath - omed love di -

vine, reign thou with- in my heart; from thee nor depth nor height, nor life, nor death can

part; my life is hid in God with thee, now and through all e -

ter - ni - ty, now and through

all e - ter - ni - ty.

# O FOR A CLOSER WALK

Text: William Cowper (1731-1800)
Music: Charles Villiers Stanford (1852-1924) arr. Alan Ridout

mourn,        and    drove    thee     from my   breast.

*mf* So   shall   my   walk   be    close with God,

So      shall   my   walk   be

close with God, calm     and   se-rene      my    frame;

so pu – rer light shall mark the road

that leads me to the Lamb.

that leads me to the Lamb.

# Anthems

# O FOR THE WINGS OF A DOVE

Text: Psalm 55:6-7
Music: Felix Mendelssohn (1809-1847) arr. Colin Hand

way would I rove. O for the wings, for the wings of a dove!

way would I rove. O for the wings, for the wings of a dove!

way would I rove. O for the wings, for the wings of a dove!

Far a - way, far a - way, far a - way, far a - way would I rove, in the

Far a - way, far a - way, far a - way, far a - way would I rove,

Far a - way, far a - way, far a - way, far a - way would I rove,

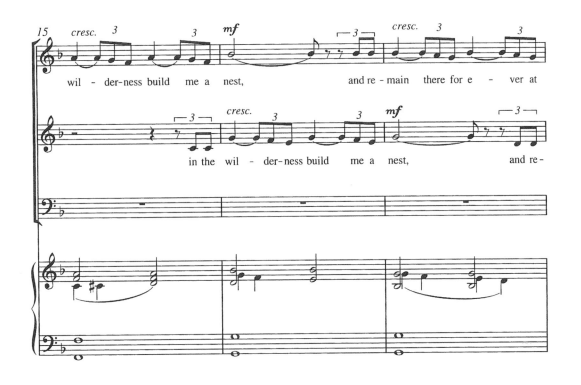

and re - main there for e - ver at rest; in the wil - der - ness

and re - main there for e - ver at rest; in the wil - der - ness

and re - main there for e - ver at rest; in the wil - der - ness

build me a nest, and re - main there for e - ver at rest,

build me a nest, and re - main there for e - ver at rest,

build me a nest, and re - main there for e - ver at rest,

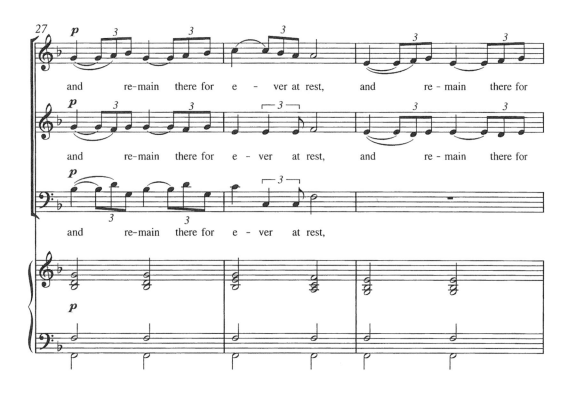

and re-main there for e - ver at rest, and re-main there for

and re-main there for e - ver at rest, and re - main there for

and re-main there for e - ver at rest,

e - ver at rest.

e - ver at rest.

for e - ver at rest.

# O GREAT, ALL-SEEING GOD

Text: Michael Forster (b.1946)
Music: Andrew Moore (b.1954)

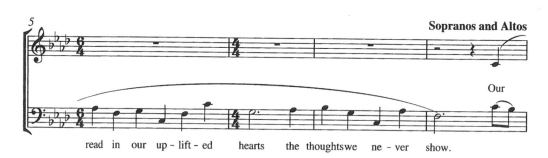

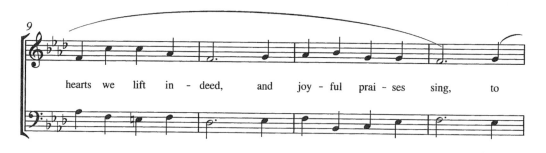

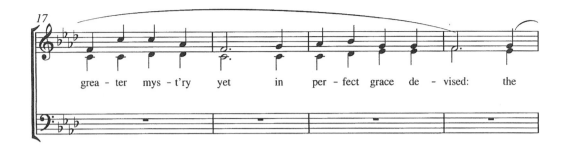

grea - ter mys - t'ry yet in per - fect grace de - vised: the

fa - ther's own be - lov - ed son by hu - man hand bap - tised! O

grace be - yond com - pare, and ma - je - sty un - known: to

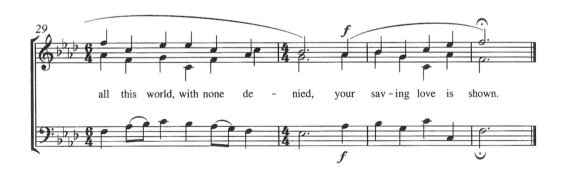

all this world, with none de - nied, your sav - ing love is shown.

# O JESU, JOY OF LOVING HEARTS

Text: 12th century Latin, translated by Ray Palmer (1808-1887)
Music: from the Plainsong 'Jesu dulcis memoria', arranged by Stanley Vann (b.1910)

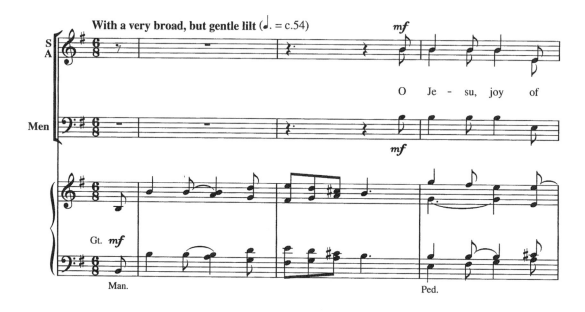

we seek the peace your love im - parts, and stand re - joi - cing in your sight.

Altos
We taste in you our liv-ing bread and

Men

357

faith   can   hold   you   fast.

Man.

**Full choir**

*f*

S
A

O

Men

*f*

add

Gt. *f*

Ped.

Je - su, e - ver with us   stay,   make   all   our   mo - ments

calm and bright; O

chase the night of sin a - way, shed o'er the world your

*molto rall.*

*ff*

ho - ly light.

# O KING, AND DESIRE OF ALL NATIONS

Text: From the Latin *O Antiphon*
Music: John Stainer (1840-1901) arr. Alan Ridout

come and save man, whom thou form‑edst from the clay, come and save man, whom thou form‑edst from the clay, come and save man, whom thou form‑edst from the clay, come, Lord Je‑sus, come!

Man.

# O LEAVE ME NOT, MY EVER-LOVING GOD

Text: Unknown
Music: Johann Sebastian Bach (1685-1750) arr. Alan Ridout

God;            hear       in      high   heav'n          my
I.              Soon       I      must   drink          death's

plead  -  ing,    grant     to      me     peace          and
po  -  tion,      come      to      the    throne         for

com  -  fort,    when    I     with    grief    low    am    laid.
judge  -  ment,  where - in    the    Book     all    is    writ.

# Anthems

# ON THIS MOUNTAIN

Text: Isaiah 25:6-7
Music: Alan Ridout (1934-1996)

will des-troy death    for  e  -  ver,

for    e  -  ver.

# O SAVIOUR OF THE WORLD

Text: From The Book of Common Prayer
Music: John Goss (1800-1880) arr. Alan Ridout

blood hast re - deem - ed us, Save us and help us, we
hum - bly be - seech thee, O Lord, O save us, save us and
help us, we hum - bly be - seech thee, O Lord. A - men, A - men.

O Sa - viour of the world,

# O SAVIOUR OF THE WORLD

Text: From The Book of Common Prayer
Music: Arthur Somervell (1863-1937) arr. Alan Ridout

Sa - viour of the world, who by thy cross and pre - cious blood hast re - deem — ed

Sa - viour of the world, who by thy cross and pre - cious blood hast re - deem — ed

Sa - viour of the world, who by thy cross and pre - cious blood hast re - deem — ed

us, save us and help us,

us, save us and help us, we hum - bly be -

us, save us and help us, and help us, we hum - bly be -

save us and help us, we hum - bly be - seech thee. O

seech thee, we hum-bly, we hum - bly be - seech thee. O

seech thee, we hum-bly, we hum - bly be - seech thee. O

Sa - viour of the world, O Sa - viour of the world, who by thy cross and pre - cious

Sa - viour of the world, O Sa - viour of the world, who by thy cross and pre - cious

Sa - viour of the world, O Sa - viour of the world, who by thy cross and pre - cious

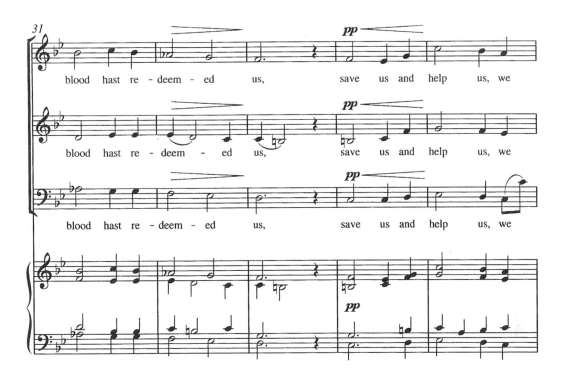

blood hast re - deem - ed us, save us and help us, we

blood hast re - deem - ed us, save us and help us, we

blood hast re - deem - ed us, save us and help us, we

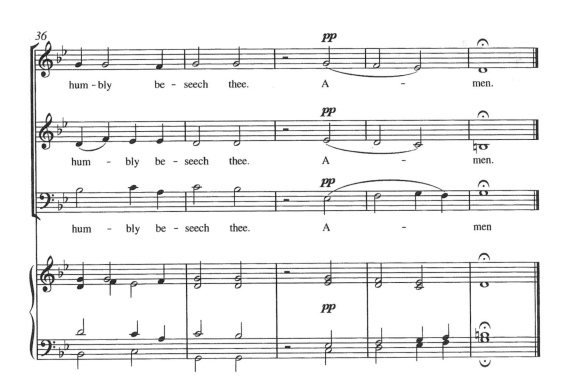

hum - bly be - seech thee. A - men.

hum - bly be - seech thee. A - men.

hum - bly be - seech thee. A - men

# O SHOUT TO THE LORD IN TRIUMPH

Text: Adapted from Psalm 100
Music: Christopher Tambling (b.1964)

Ju - bi - la - te, ju - bi - la - te De - o!

O be joy - ful in the Lord!

Come in - to his gates with thanks - giv - ing and in - to his courts with

Come in - to his gates with thanks - giv - ing and in - to his courts with

praise: give thanks to him and bless his ho - ly

# O TASTE AND SEE

Text: Psalm 34: 8-9
Music: John Goss (1800-1880) arr. Alan Ridout

# O THOU THE CENTRAL ORB

Text: Henry Ramsden Bramley (1833-1917)
Music: Charles Wood (1866-1926) arr. Alan Ridout

# PANIS ANGELICUS

Text: Thomas Aquinas (1227-1274)
Music: Marc-Antoine Charpentier (1645-1704) arr. Alan Ridout

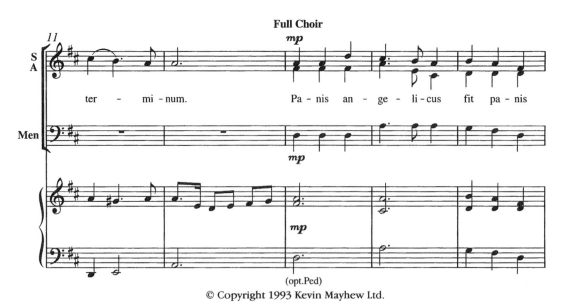

(opt.Ped)

Ser - vus pau - per et hu — mi - lis. O res mi -

ra - bi-lis! O, O, O res mi - ra - bi - lis!

# PANIS ANGELICUS

Text: Thomas Aquinas (1227-1274)
Music: César Franck (1822-1890) arr. Alan Ridout

pau - per, pau - per, ser - vus, ser - vus et
hu - mi - lis.

# PIE JESU

Text: from the Requiem Mass
Music: Gabriel Fauré (1845-1924) arr. Alan Ridout

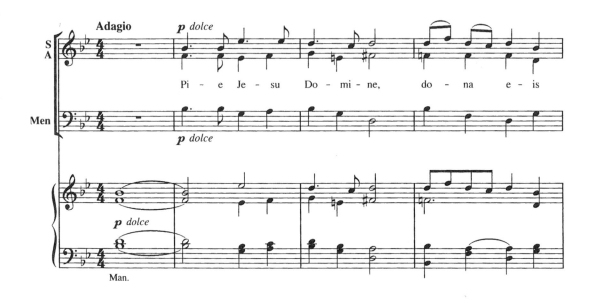

Pi - e, pi - e Je - su, pi - e Je - su Do - mi - ne,

do - na e - is, do - na e - is sem - pi - ter - nam

re - qui-em, sem - pi - ter - nam re - qui - em.

# PRAISE TO GOD, IMMORTAL PRAISE

Text: Anna Laetitia Barbauld (1734-1825)
Music: Stanley Vann (b. 1910)

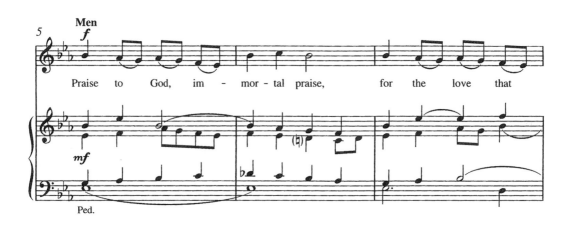

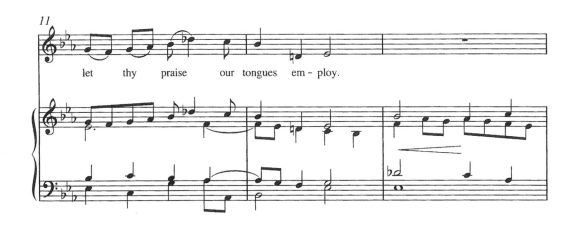

let thy praise our tongues em - ploy.

**Sopranos and Altos**
*mp*

All that spring with

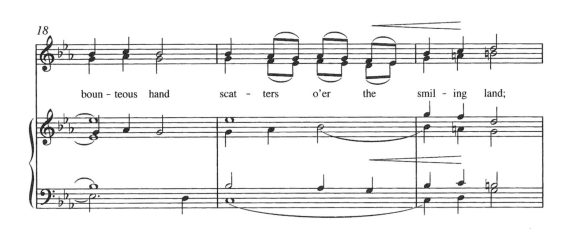

boun - teous hand scat - ters o'er the smil - ing land;

all that lib - 'ral au - tumn pours from her rich o'er - flow - ing stores.

Man.

*poco meno mosso*

*rall.*

**Maestoso**

**Descant**

These to thee, my God, we owe: source whence all our

**Altos and Men**

# PROCLAIM THE STORY

Text: Nick Fawcett
Music: Te Deum Prelude – Marc-Antoine Charpentier (1636-1704)
arr. Noel Rawsthorne

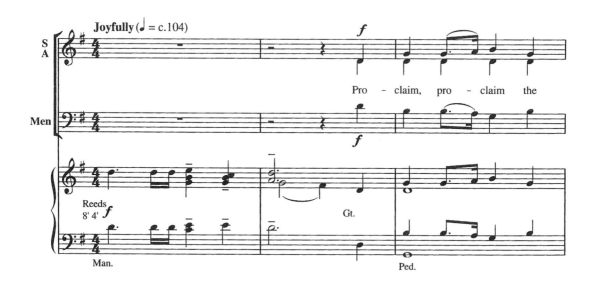

known to all his glo - ry, lift up his name on

high!

He comes to reign for e-ver-more, come
kneel, a-dore, bow down in awe; lift up your hearts and
wor-ship Christ, whom God has crowned as Lord!

**Broader**

Sing out, sing out ho - san - na! Re -

joice and greet the King of kings! Lift high his roy - al ban - ner, lift up your voice and sing.

# SING ALOUD, THE DAY IS BREAKING

Text: Nick Fawcett
Music: Ode to Joy – Ludwig van Beethoven (1770-1827)
arr. Noel Rawsthorne

Sing a-loud, the day is break-ing, sun-shine bathes the world in light,

all a-round the earth is wak-ing, morn-ing's pro-mise af-ter night.

Birds are call-ing, songs en-thrall-ing, fill the air with psalms of praise, in

the ci-ty sud-den bus-tle, in the mea-dow cat-tle graze.
in the ci-ty

Dew drops glis-ten, gent-ly chris-ten life re-newed and hope re-born; ce-

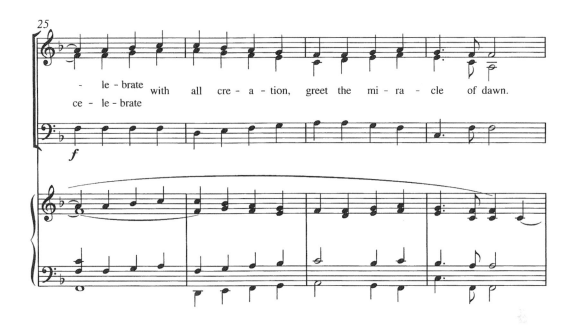

-le - brate with all cre - a - tion, greet the mi - ra - cle of dawn.
ce - le - brate

dim.

**Sopranos and Altos**

Sing a - loud, the night is end - ed, morn - ing bathes the world with joy,

sin and death have been trans-cend-ed, no-thing now can hope des-troy.

Shin-ing af-ter tears comes laugh-ter, bro-ken hearts be-gin to heal, grave-

- clothes ly - ing neat-ly fold-ed, can what they pro-claim be real?
grave-clothes ly - ing

Mist is clear-ing, faith ap - pear-ing, con - quers fear and scat - ters gloom, ce -

- le - brate with all cre - a - tion: Christ is ris - en from the tomb!
ce - le - brate with

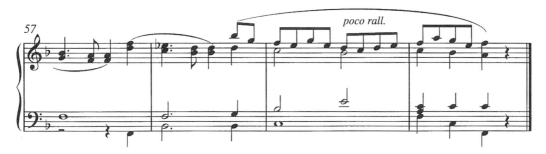

# Anthems

*For Prebendary EEF Walters on attaining four-score years and ten*

# SING PRAISE TO GOD

Text: Johann Schütz (1640-1690)
Music: Richard Lloyd (b.1933)

God of love, the God of our sal -

va - tion; with heal - ing balm my soul he fills,

Man.

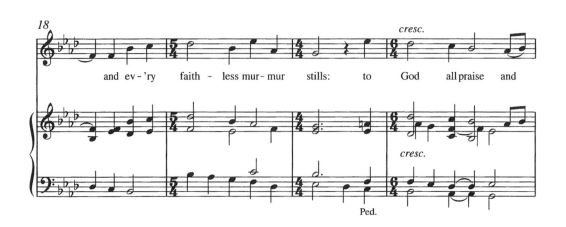

and ev - 'ry faith - less mur - mur stills: to God all praise and

Ped.

praise and glo - ry!

Then

all my glad-some way a - long

I sing thy

I sing a - loud thy

praises, that men may hear the grateful song my voice unwearied raises;

grateful song my voice unwearied raises;

be joyful in the Lord, my heart; both soul and

# SING TO GOD A SONG OF GLADNESS

Text: Michael Forster (b.1946)
Music: Andrew Moore (b.1954)

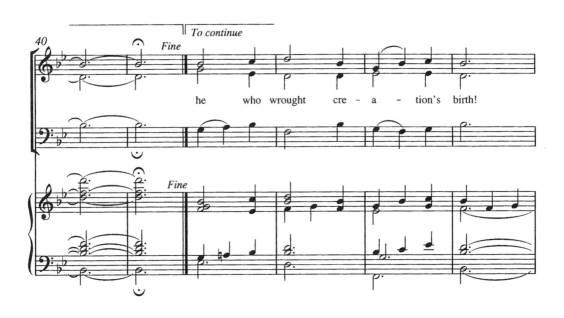

ho - ly church di - vide, we are called to true com - mu - nion in the light of him who died.

# SPEAK PEACE

Text: Mary MacDonald
Music: Rosalie Bonighton (b.1946)

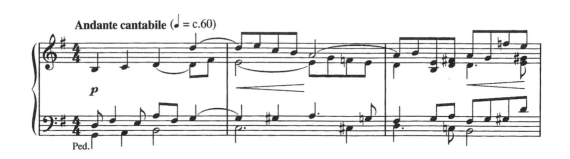

thoughts, speak peace, speak peace, al - migh - ty God.

peace, peace to my trou - bled thoughts, al - migh - ty God.

Speak peace, speak peace to my trou - bled thoughts, al - migh - ty God.

Man.

poco rit.    a tempo

S
A

Still me, that I may

Men

Still me,

poco rit.    a tempo

Ped.

you

you

in the way,       in the way    of    love.

# Anthems

# TEACH ME, O LORD

Text: Psalm 119:33
Music: Thomas Attwood (1765-1838) arr. Alan Ridout

449

# THE HEAVENS ARE TELLING

Text: Psalm 19:1-4
Music: Joseph Haydn (1732-1809) arr. Alan Ridout

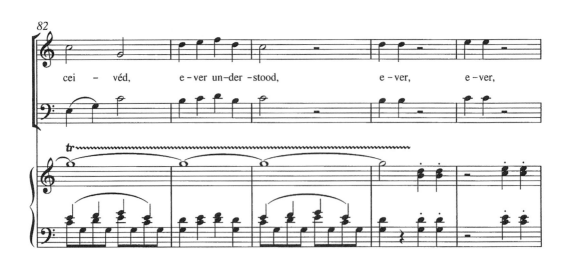

# THE HOLY VINE

Text: John 15
Music: Andrew Moore (b. 1954)

# THE LORD'S PRAYER

Text: Matthew 6:9-14
Music: Robert Stone (1516-1613) arr. Alan Ridout

# Anthems

# THE WILL OF GOD

Text: Timothy Dudley-Smith (b.1926)
Music: Norman Warren (b.1934)

1. The will of God to mark my way, the word of God for light;
2. Your eyes of mer-cy keep me still, your gra-cious love be mine;

cure and strong, from man's op-pres-sion freed, re - deemed from ev - 'ry

kind of wrong in thought and word and deed.

Ped.

4. So set my heart to

walk with truth be - fore the Lord in right - eous-ness, in

in righ - eous-ness,

right - eous-ness and love.

Ped.

*For Stephen Bydder and the choir of Scots College*

# THOU, O GOD, ART PRAISED IN SION

Text: Psalm 65: 1, 2
Music: June Nixon

come.

# THOU VISITEST THE EARTH

Text: from Psalm 65
Music: Maurice Green (c.1694-1755) arr. Alan Ridout

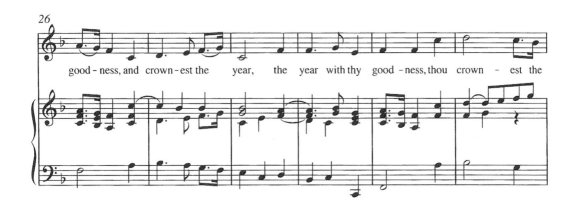

good - ness, and crown - est the year, the year with thy good - ness, thou crown - est the

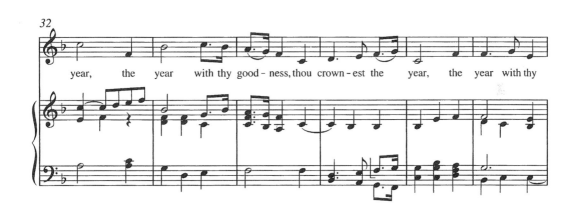

year, the year with thy good - ness, thou crown - est the year, the year with thy

**All**
*mf*

S  good-ness. Thou vi - sit-est the earth and bles-sest it, and bles-sest it; and

A  *mf*  Thou vi - sit-est the earth and bles-sest it; and

Men  *mf*  Thou vi - sit-est the earth and bles-sest it; and

*mf*

Ped.

# THOU WILT KEEP HIM IN PERFECT PEACE

Text: from Scripture
Music: Samuel Sebastian Wesley (1810-1876) arr. Alan Ridout

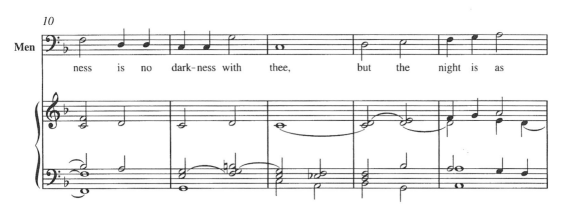

Men: ness is no dark-ness with thee, but the night is as

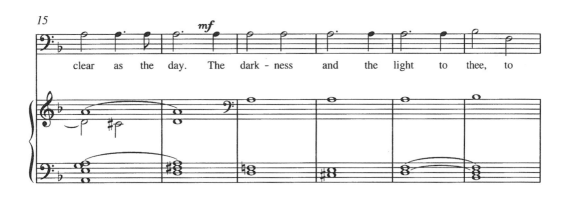

clear as the day. The dark - ness and the light to thee, to

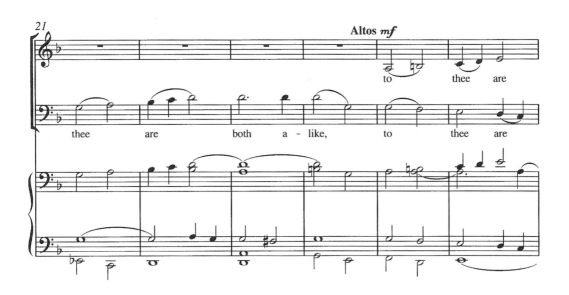

Altos *mf*

to thee are

thee are both a - like, to thee are

488

# TIMELESS LOVE

Text: Timothy Dudley-Smith (b.1926)
Music: Norman Warren (b.1934)

word. Who is like him? Praise the Lord!

Truth and right - eous - ness en - throne him, just and

493

# TOLLITE HOSTIAS

Latin Text: Psalm 96:8, 9, 11, 13
English Text: John Ballantine (b.1942)
Music: Camille Saint-Saëns (1835-1921) arr. Alan Ridout

Læ - ten - tur cæ - li et ex - ul - tet ter - ra,
*Earth and the hea - vens re - joice in his great - ness,*

a fa - ci - e Do - mi - ni, quo - ni - am ve - nit, al - le - lu - ia.
*wor - ship the Lord of the worlds who will come to save,*
quo - ni - am ve - nit, al - le - lu - ia, al - le - lu - ia.
*he will come to save, al - le - lu - ia, al - le - lu - ia.*

Læ - ten - tur cæ - li et ex - ul - tet ter - ra
*Earth and the hea - vens re - joice in his great - ness.*

# TURN THY FACE FROM MY SINS

Text: from Psalm 51
Music: Thomas Attwood (1765-1838) arr. Alan Ridout

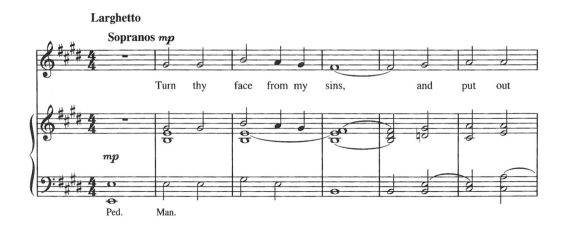

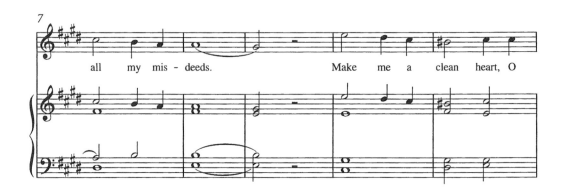

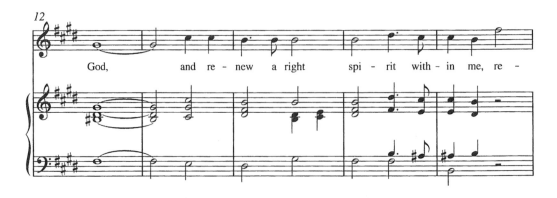

new, re - new, re - new, re - new a right spi - rit with-

in me, re - new a right spi - rit with - in me.

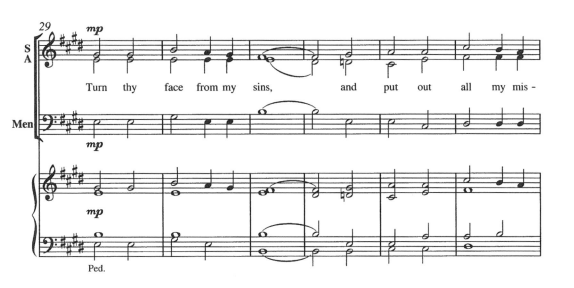

Turn thy face from my sins, and put out all my mis-

# WALKING BY FAITH

Text: John Raphael Peacey (1896-1971)
Music: John Marsh (b.1939)

we de-lay and doubt your pow'r to raise the dead.

Yet with you we will firm-ly stay: you are the

Truth, the Life, the Way.

love's as - sur - ance we con - fide. Now we be - lieve, that we may

love's as - sur - ance we con - fide. Now we be - lieve, that we may

love's as - sur - ance we con - fide. Now we be - lieve, that we may

know, and in that know - ledge dai - ly grow.

know, and in that know - ledge dai - ly grow.

know, and in that know - ledge dai - ly grow.

# WHAT PRAISE, WHAT GLORY

Text: Brian Foley (b.1919)
Music: Andrew Fletcher (b.1950)

# WHEN MUSIC WAKES MY SLEEPING HEART

Text: Delores Dufner, OSB (b.1939)
Music: Rosalie Bonighton (b.1946)

ev - 'ry breath, and ev - 'ry breath, ev - 'ry breath a song.

ev - 'ry breath

When mu - sic

ga - thers us in prayer and sum - mons us to

praise, then beau-ty spills her shin-ing light a - cross our dark - ened days.

When mu - sic fills the u - ni - verse and all is me - lo -

dy,  then Christ the Lord will lead a hymn of soar - ing ma- je - sty:

'All hon - our  to the Ho - ly One,  all praise and glo - ry

# ZADOK THE PRIEST

Text: from Scripture
Music: George Frideric Handel (1685-1759) arr. Colin Hand